THE MENORAH

JUMBO COLORING AND ACTIVITY BOOK

bendon®

Bendon, Inc. All rights reserved.
The BENDON name, logo, and Tear and Share are
trademarks of Bendon, Inc. Ashland, OH 44805.

What is Hanukkah?

The history of Hanukkah, the Festival of Lights, comes from an ancient text. Over 2,000 years ago, a king named Antiochus IV Epiphanes invaded the land of Judea. He wanted all of the people living there to convert to his religion. He made laws that meant the Jewish people could not practice their religion anymore. He took over their holy Temple and dedicated it to the Greek god Zeus. Led by a family called the Maccabees, the Jewish people decided to fight back. It took years, but they finally defeated the army of Antiochus IV. They cleansed their Temple, installed a new altar, and rededicated it. According to Jewish teachings, there was only one small jar of holy oil left in the Temple that had not been ruined by Antiochus. It only had enough oil to light the Temple for one day, but it burned for eight days and nights until new sacred oil could be found. Today, families all over the world celebrate the rededication of the Temple and the miracles of Hanukkah with a joyous festival lasting eight days.

Let's Count!

How many candles do you count?

Your Answer:

Words of Wisdom

How many words can you make using the letters in

FESTIVAL OF LIGHTS?

_____   _____

_____   _____

_____   _____

_____   _____

_____   _____

_____   _____

_____   _____

_____

_____

_____

I love to hear the story of Hanukkah!

Matching

Draw lines connecting the matching objects.

Let's Draw!

Draw a picture of your favorite Hanukkah tradition.

Crack the Code

Use the code key to fill in the blanks and decipher the secret message.

Many families give Hanukkah gelt to children.

Let's Draw!

Use the grid as a guide to draw the gelt in the space below.

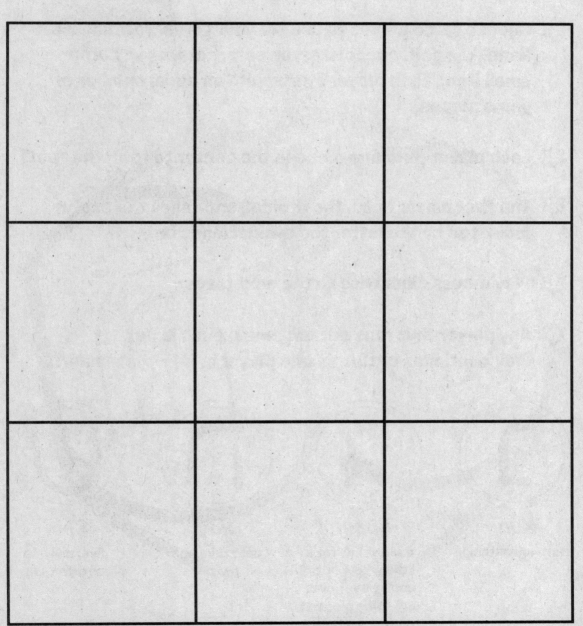

Let's Play Dreidel!

A dreidel is a four-sided spinning top, usually made of wood or plastic. On each of the four sides is a Hebrew letter–*nun, gimel, hey,* and *shin.* The letters form an acronym of the Hebrew phrase *Nes gadol hayah sham,* meaning "a great miracle happened there". Dreidel is a popular game that is traditionally played at Hanukkah.

How to Play:

✡ Choose game pieces to use for your game. You can use Hanukkah gelt, chocolates, sweets, nuts, or any other small item. Each player starts with an equal number of game pieces.

✡ Each player puts one piece in the center to form the "pot".

✡ The first player spins the dreidel, and takes the action indicated by the letter the dreidel lands on.

✡ Play moves clockwise to the next player.

✡ Any player that runs out of game pieces is out. Play continues until only one player is left–the winner!

Nun	*Gimel*	*Hey*	*Shin*
nothing; nothing	everything; take the whole pot, each player puts one game piece in to start a new pot	half; take half the pot	give; put one piece into the pot

Make Your Own Paper Dreidel

fold in

fold in

fold in

Nun
nothing

Gimel
everything

fold in

Hey
half

fold in

Shin
give

fold in

fold in

Directions

1. Carefully cut along the black outer line.

2. Fold along the gray dotted lines.

3. Tape the fold in tabs to the inside to form the shape of your dreidel.

4. Push a pencil or straw through the top circle, all the way to the bottom.

5. Spin to win!

Tic-Tac-Toe

Challenge your family and friends!

Find It Fast!

**Most menorahs have seven arms, but the Hanukkah menorah has nine.
Can you spot the Hanukkah menorah?**

Some families exchange gifts at Hanukkah.

Rhyme Time!

How many words can you think of that rhyme with

LIGHT?

_____   _____

_____   _____

_____   _____

_____   _____

_____   _____

_____

_____

_____

Words of Wisdom

How many words can you make using the letters in

MACCABEES?

Printing Practice

Color the picture and practice printing the word.

FAMILY

Squares

H
example

Challenge a friend to a game and take turns drawing a line from one dot to another. If you make a line that completes a square, put your initial inside that box. The player with the most squares at the end of the game wins!

Same & Different

Which two menorahs are the same?

A

B

C

D

Your Answers:

&

Word Search

Find and circle the Hanukkah words in the puzzle.

altar	Judah	perseverance
Antiochus	Maccabees	temple
dedication	miracle	
eight	oil	

```
P R M A N T I O C H U S H O
E M B Y T C G Z V B K D S K
R A J C P L H E C R H E N B
S N V U R A T O T I O D S A
E S A M D H J R E E R I P L
V K P D G A L B M A P C L T
E T C I S E H C P I Y A D A
R A E O P S Q T L G D T T R
A R M I R A C L E M L I R M
N A K H W N T R Q D N O L A
C A S E F G E R I V A N S S
E B R Y P M A C C A B E E S
```

Let's Draw!

Use the grid as a guide to draw the Hanukkah menorah in the space below.

Let's spin the dreidel!

Word Scramble

Unscramble the letters to correctly spell the Hanukkah words.

N O M E R H A

R I A T D T O N I

A C N S D E L

G I H L T

H S M A H A S

Printing Practice

Color the picture and practice printing the word.

MENORAH

DREIDEL DREIDEL DREIDEL

Word Scramble

Unscramble the letters to correctly spell the Hanukkah words.

L P E M E T

A B A M E C S E C

C D I A N D T E I O

R I C A M E L

L A T R A

I L O

Let's Count!

How many coins do you count?

Your Answer:

Matching

Draw lines connecting the matching objects.

Tic-Tac-Toe

Challenge your family and friends!

Lighting the menorah is one of the most important Hanukkah traditions.

Printing Practice

Color the picture and practice printing the word.

HANUKKAH

NES GADOL HAYAH SHAM.

Let's Draw!

Use the grid as a guide to draw the candle in the space below.

A-Maze-ing!

Find your way through the maze to get the shamash
to the menorah to light the Hanukkah candles!

START

FINISH

Squares

example

Challenge a friend to a game and take turns drawing a line from one dot to another. If you make a line that completes a square, put your initial inside that box. The player with the most squares at the end of the game wins!

We give thanks for the miracle of Hanukkah.

Get Creative!

Write about some of your favorite Hanukkah traditions.

_____

_____

_____

_____

_____

_____

_____

_____

_____

_____

_____

Menorah Math

For the first night of Hanukkah, you'll need a shamash and one candle to light your Hanukkah menorah. On the second night, you'll need a shamash and two candles. How many candles will you need to celebrate all eight nights of Hanukkah?

Night 1 🕯 + 🕯 = ☐

Night 2 🕯 + 🕯 + 🕯 = ☐

Night 3 🕯 + 🕯 + 🕯 + 🕯 = ☐

Night 4 🕯 + 🕯 + 🕯 + 🕯 + 🕯 = ☐

Night 5 🕯 + 🕯 + 🕯 + 🕯 + 🕯 + 🕯 = ☐

Night 6 🕯 + 🕯 + 🕯 + 🕯 + 🕯 + 🕯 + 🕯 = ☐

Night 7 🕯 + 🕯 + 🕯 + 🕯 + 🕯 + 🕯 + 🕯 + 🕯 = ☐

Night 8 🕯 + 🕯 + 🕯 + 🕯 + 🕯 + 🕯 + 🕯 + 🕯 + 🕯 = ☐

Total number of candles = ☐

Sudoku

Can you complete these Hanukkah sudoku puzzles?
Each image should appear only once in each row and each column.

Words to Know!

Chag same'ach - Hebrew for "happy holiday"

dreidel - a four-sided top marked with Hebrew letters and used to play a game, traditionally at Hanukkah

gelt - money, often given to children at Hanukkah wrapped in gold foil

gimel - the third letter of the Hebrew alphabet

Hanukkah - eight-night Jewish festival celebrating the rededication of the Temple

hey - the fifth letter of the Hebrew alphabet

latkes - fried potato pancakes, usually served at Hanukkah

menorah - a candelabra used in Jewish worship

nes gadol hayah sham - Hebrew for "a great miracle happened there"

nun - the fourteenth letter of the Hebrew alphabet

shamash - candle used to light the other candles on a menorah, also called the attendant or servant candle

shin - the twenty-first letter of the Hebrew alphabet

sufganiyot - fried jelly doughnut, usually served at Hanukkah

tzedakah - gifts of kindness, service, or charity, from the Hebrew word for righteousness